WHISTLE PUNK
MADE THIS
MAP
OF THE
THE AJAX LUMBER COMPANY'S
WORKINGS

Lumbercamp

By GLEN ROUNDS

Being the *Life* and
Good Times of the new

WHISTLE PUNK

at Camp Fifteen
up Horse Crick Way, with
many *Drawings* made on
the Scene by the *Author*

HOLIDAY HOUSE, 1937, New York

To
M. E. M. O.

INTRODUCTION

OL' FORTY-TWO was a proud new locomotive when I first met her. Off and on for a long time I'd been working for the Warren Lamb Lumber Company, and was gandy dancin' on their narrow gauge line the rainy fall night they brought her up on her trial run with Bristoe Hood, Johnnie Skaggs and some other brass hats aboard, and she tore out a rail on the curve above Camp One.

Last summer I went back to make these drawings and found her still making her daily trips and as cantankerous as ever, burning the seat of my britches at every opportunity, as if I had been a greenhorn like Whistle Punk.

But I forgave her, and rode up and down the line in her greasy cab from camp to mill and back again, making drawings of the operations and men I used to know, and listening again to tall stories in the bunk houses nights. Most of the men in "Lumbercamp" I used to know, and Whistle Punk might be any one of the greenhorns that I have seen drift in and out of camps.

Caterpillar tractors, Diesel engines, motor trucks, and electric lights in the bunk houses give evidence of the machine age, but so far have failed to rob logging of its colorful, rough and tumble atmosphere. It still takes a strong back to be a lumberjack.

Glen Rounds
New York City, September 1, 1937

CONTENTS

CHAPTER I: The Greenhorn shows up. Gets him a new Moniker. Meets Ol' Forty-two. Heads for the Timber riding in the Cab. Scorches the Seat of his Britches. Round hairpin Turns. Sees the Gandy Dancers.   11

CHAPTER II: Whistle Punk hits Camp Fifteen mighty footsore. The Boss is not Impressed. Listens to the Bull Cook's wild Tale. 'Rassles Mattress and Soogans in the Bunk House. Tries on tin Pants.   27

CHAPTER III: Whistle Punk tries to look like an Oldtimer. Grub Pile! Gets wise to Mess Hall Etiquette. Back to the Bunk House. Hears a Sidehill Whiffler Holler. Learns how to defend himself.   43

CHAPTER IV: Whiffle Stick. The Kid works himself into a Lather. Struggles up the Tote Road with his Equipment. What a Bulldozer is. Rosinbelly tops the Spar Tree. Is put to swamping.   53

CHAPTER V: A real Whistle Punk at last! Step-and-a-half starts him off. How the High Lead works. Signals. How Paul Bunyan lost a cutting Crew in Kansas, and built the biggest Dragline ever built.   67

CHAPTER VI: Forest Fire! Whistle Punk is rarin' to go. Call comes for more Men. Fire Guards in Heat and Smoke. Almost trapped. Decides Fire Fighting is not much Fun.   75

Contents, continued

CHAPTER VII: Deer on the Hillsides. Whistle Punk gets him some felt Boots. Pete Prestjohn tells how his Horses used to ride. The Eagle screams, but not for Him. Sees the Jammer work. Gets his Tail-feathers caught.   87

CHAPTER VIII: Whistle Punk finally gets his Pay and goes to Town. Takes a Bellyflop into the Mill Pond. Goes through the Big Sawmill with Shikepoke. Sees the Logs sawed into Lumber. Haircut, city Style.   101

ILLUSTRATIONS

Whistle Punk	Frontispiece
A Greenhorn Came Dusting across the Bridge	10
"I'm the New Whistle Punk."	14
It Was No Picnic Being the Extra Man	16
The Engineer Poked His Head in among the Wheels	18
The Front End of the Train Came in Sight	20
Gandy Dancers	22
On Spider-legged Little Trestles	24
Camp Fifteen	26
Polishing the Top of His Bald Head	28
A Stove Made from a Fifty-gallon Oil Drum	32
Baldy the Bull Cook	37
The Big Bell at the Mess Hall Rang for Supper	42
Without Gigging Them with His Spikes	44
The Crew Went Back to the Bunk House	46

Illustrations, continued

The Sidehill Whiffler	48
Shikepoke	50
It Was Time to Start for Work	52
The Bulldozer	56
Rosinbelly	58
The Trees Are Cut by a Falling Crew	60
The Trunk Bucked up into Log Lengths	62
Later the Skidders Come Along	64
The Donkey Engine	66
The High Lead	70
A Big Cloud of Black Smoke Rising to the Northwest	74
Making a Fire Break	78
There Was No Time to Lose	82
They Stumbled off to the Bunk House	84
After Snow Came They Used Bobsleds	86
"Their Manes and Tails A-flyin' in the Wind"	89
Jaybird Smith	91
The Crew Gathered Round to Offer Suggestions	94
The Top Loader Grabbed It with His Cant Hook	96
The Car Might Turn Turtle on a Rough Curve	98
The Big Straddler	100
Letting the Top Logs Roll into the Pond	104
He Lost His Balance Entirely	106
The Bull Chain	108
A Tractor Pulling a Box Car	110
They All Braced Themselves for the Ride	112
A Seemingly Endless Stream of Logs	114
Expanding His Chest Somewhat	116

LUMBERCAMP

CHAPTER I: *The Greenhorn shows up. Gets him a new Moniker. Meets Ol' Forty-two. Heads for the Timber riding in the Cab. Scorches the Seat of his Britches. Round hairpin Turns. Sees the Gandy Dancers.*

A LITTLE after sunup on a frosty fall morning, a greenhorn came dusting across the bridge into the mill yard of the Ajax Lumber Company. He was all duded up in store clothes and had his hat jammed down solid onto his ears. Just a kid, he was, with no more idea about what a lumber camp was like than a pig has about a schoolhouse, but plumb busted out with ambition, nevertheless.

It being so early in the morning the mill yard looked all quiet and deserted. About the only sign of life was a brakeman puttering around the string of empty log cars by the mill pond, and the lazy clouds of steam over in front of the big mill.

The Ajax outfit, instead of floating their logs out,

had their own narrow gauge railroad connecting the mill with the camps on half a dozen watersheds. The kid was to ride the log train up, and in spite of the fact he was half an hour early, he was scared green for fear they might have gone off without him.

But after he hightailed it around the blacksmith shop to where he could see the engine shed, he found the train crew sitting on the back step of the locomotive soaking up the sun while they waited for steam.

He skidded to a stop, set his war sack down, and stood around a spell waiting for someone to notice he was there. Ol' Forty-two, the locomotive, sizzled and gurgled and hissed to herself. The engineer sat and smoked his pipe, and the fireman just sat. Nobody said a word.

Directly, however, the kid got his breath back and after hemming and hawing around a bit, decided to speak up.

"I'm the new whistle punk fer Camp Fifteen, an' Mr. Skookum Bill when he hired me yesterday told me thet I could ride up as far as the Horse Crick sidin' with yuh this mornin'," he said, speaking all in a rush.

The engineer, being anything but a hasty gent, mulled the news over in his mind a spell; then, after taking his pipe out of his mouth so he could polish his gold tooth on his sleeve, he reckoned as how it could be fixed up.

"Throw yore plunder in the cab, Bub," said he. "We'll be driftin' directly."

About that time the brakeman moseyed up, having finished his job of puttering, and looked the kid over kind of curious like.

"New feller fer Boodleman's," the engineer said to no one in particular.

"Howdy," said the brakie, who was a friendly sort of duck. "I'm Bob Smith, but more commonly knowed hereabouts as Whistle Britches. Whut's yore moniker?"

"Moniker?" said the kid, all puzzled.

"Yeah. Whut's yore handle? Whadda folks call yuh?"

"Oh, my name," grinned the kid, catching on. "I'm Axel Scheafersteinn."

"Now ain't thet a jawbreaker fer yuh?" Whistle Britches wanted to know. "Reckon yuh could answer t' Whistle Punk jest as well?"

"Sure thing!" And the kid stood there grinning from ear to ear.

He stood around a bit longer, but no one had anything more to say, so he started looking the locomotive over. She was a queer-looking contraption, he thought, with her humpbacked boiler and stubby build. And instead of the usual high drive wheels she had only a little set of trucks in front and another way back under the back end of the tender, connected by a geared drive shaft like a big old-fashioned coffee grinder.

Pretty soon the pop valve up on top cut loose, showing that steam was up. So the fireman, the engineer and Whistle Punk climbed up into the cab while the brakeman ran to open the switch that let them onto the track where the empty train sat. After hooking onto the empties they pulled out on the main line with a great chuffing and hissing and clanking.

As they went past the mill-hands' shacks along the edge of town Whistle Punk hung out of the door of the cab watching for folks to wave at. But once they got out in the open he was kept plenty busy trying to keep out from under foot as they rocked around the curves of the big canyon at seven miles

an hour. He soon came to the conclusion that it was no picnic being the extra man in a little cab like that, especially when the track was so rough.

He'd reach out to grab something to steady himself and find that he'd glommed onto a hot injector pipe or something. When he jerked loose from that

16

his feet were more than likely to slip on the greasy gangway plates and he'd find the seat of his pants sizzling against the fire-box door.

After they'd been out a while the fireman came back from where he sat among his gauges and gadgets on the left side of the cab, and poured a couple scoops full of sand through the hole in the fire-box door, to scrape the soot out of the flues.

That gave Whistle Punk the idea of trying to look into the fire-box himself. But just as he got his eye down to it a back draft blew a puff of flame and smoke out into his face. It didn't damage him any, but blacked him up some and didn't do his eyebrows any particular good.

So, what with one thing and another, by the time they hammered through the narrow cut in the solid rock that led into Camp One, he was a sight for sore eyes any way you figured it.

The camp was set back on the level floor of the big canyon, between the river and the high cliffs of the canyon wall. This had once been a busy logging

Lumbercamp

camp, but since operations had been pushed on back into the hills it was used only by the section crew working on the tracks. All that was left were a couple of tar-papered shacks, some side-tracks for extra rolling stock, and a water tower.

The train ground and clanked to a stop, and the locomotive was unhooked and switched into another track so she could be run back to the water tower. While the fireman filled the tank on the tender, the engineer poked his head in among the wheels, tightened a few bolts and squirted a little oil here and there.

When all these odd jobs were finished, they ran the locomotive on back, and threw another switch that brought them out on the main line behind the string of empties. Then, pushing the string in front of them, they started up a little side canyon that would finally lead them out on top of the divide.

The business of pushing the cars ahead looked kind of foolish to Whistle Punk, especially on such crooked track. The canyon here was so narrow that

19

Lumbercamp

Pushing Up

bushes growing in the cracks in the canyon wall brushed inside the cab windows. The curves were so sharp that most of the time the first car ahead was all that could be seen of the train, and that one mostly hidden by brush. Then there were hairpin turns where the front end of the train came in sight on the other side of the gully, coming back towards them.

By this time Whistle Punk's ears were accustomed to the racket of the exhaust so he could talk to the fireman.

"How come yuh push this here string instead of pullin' her?" he hollered.

"We allus push 'em on these steep grades," shouted the fireman. "Cause if'n we don't a couplin' is apt t' break an' let a car er two start runnin' wild fer the bottom. An' the grade is so steep thet before a car goes more'n forty rods she's travellin' jest too blamed fast t' make the curves. Then she jest takes off through the treetops fer the bottom of the canyon. Naturally thet don't do the car no particular good,

21

so the roadmaster gives us fits." The fireman turned a gadget or two, spit a stream of tobacco juice at a magpie flying past, and went on. "An' another thing, a wild car comin' round a bend all of a suddent like, onto where a bunch of gandy dancers are workin', is more than apt t' scare the pants off'n them an' make 'em purty dissatisfied with their jobs!"

"Gosh!" said Whistle Punk, jerking the seat of his pants off the fire-box door again. "An' whut's a gandy dancer, anyways?"

Gandy Dancers

"Gandy dancers is section hands. The fellers that yuh see tampin' ballast under the ties t' level up the track," said the fireman, yanking on the whistle cord to wake up the engineer, who had dozed off.

The engineer woke up and pushed the throttle ahead another notch, then pulled it back to where it was, and sighted out the window to see how fast they were moving. From the noise Ol' Forty-two was making they should have been doing at least forty miles an hour, but they were actually making about two and a half. So it really didn't make a whole lot of difference if the engineer did take an occasional nap.

After about an hour and a half they came out on top of the divide. Looking back they could see Camp One about a mile away in a straight line, most of it straight down. But they had travelled about six miles, the way they'd had to twist and turn around the sides of the canyon.

By the end of the morning Whistle Punk's eyes were popping out like a tromped-on frog's. First

Lumbercamp

they'd come out on top of a hogback where they could
see for miles out over the foot-hills, then they'd head
out through somebody's hay meadow before drop-
ping down into another canyon where they'd cross

and recross the swift mountain creeks on spider-
legged little trestles, from which they could look
down and see trout swimming in the clear water.

About noon they hit the Horse Creek siding. That
was as far as the train went. The empty string of
cars was to be left for the jammer crew to pick up and
load the next day, and a loaded train was waiting to
be hauled back to the mill that afternoon.

It was still about six miles to Camp Fifteen, and
the only way to get there was to walk. So Whistle
Punk said "So long!" to the train crew, hitched up
his britches, and lit out.

ABOUT the middle of the afternoon

Whistle Punk sighted the camp, and turned off the ties onto the road leading in between red painted camp buildings. By that time his feet felt like they must be blistered almost to his knees.

As he shuffled along through the deep dust he looked the camp over. On his right was the wash house, the cook shack and the mess hall. Across the road was the commissary, the office, a couple of open-faced sheds and the bunk houses. Clear on at the back were the stables and the blacksmith shop.

Nobody was in sight, so he crossed the road to the office, and walked in, stomping tol'able hard on his heels so the boss would know that he was not scared to speak of.

Lumbercamp

The boss sat with his feet on an old desk, polishing the top of his bald head with one hand while he fished around through his pockets with the other. When Whistle Punk came in he looked up but didn't stop

what he was doing. Being as how the boss said nothing the kid figured it was likely he was thinking about
something or other so he said nothing, too.

While he waited he looked the office over. That
didn't take long, as it was just a big, bare room with
a couple of axes and a cross-cut saw standing in the
corner, some odds and ends of work clothes hanging
on nails around the room, and a C. M. Russell calen-
dar on the wall. After he spotted these, there was
nothing to see but a big spider in the corner of the
window getting a last meal before cold weather came
to freeze him up. The fly he had caught raised plenty
of fuss, but the spider seemed to know his business
and soon had him roped and hog-tied. Just as the
spider threw the last hitch on the fly and sat back to
rest a bit before finishing him off, the boss found his
can of Copenhagen, which was what he had been
looking for all the time. He took himself a big chaw,
then hauled his feet down off the desk. He seemed to
be ready to talk turkey at last. After taking a couple
trial shots at a big red ant and finally putting him

29

out of business with a direct hit, he spoke up.

"Well, Bub, whut kin I do fer you?"

"I'm the new whistle punk," said the kid.

"Yuh don't say!" muttered the boss, kind of absent-minded like, paring his fingernails with a big jack-knife. "And whut's yore name?"

"My real name is Axel Scheafersteinn, but the fellers calls me Whistle Punk, bein' as the other's hard t' say."

"Yeah, reckon it is a mite easier on the jaws, all right. The bull cook will fix yuh up with blankets an' find you a bunk. Yuh kin start work in the morning."

Then he stomped to the door and hollered. "Hey you, Baldy! Come a-runnin'!"

While they waited for Baldy to show up, the boss looked the kid over, and noticing his store clothes, finally allowed, "Soon's yuh get yore plunder put away yuh better go over t' the commissary an' draw whut clothes yuh need." Then when Baldy shuffled in he went on, "Fix the kid up in the bunk house,

Bull Cook

willya Baldy? Reckon yuh better put him in the north side. No use puttin' him in with the teamsters as long as he don't seem to be much used t' bugs."

So the bull cook got some blankets and the kid followed him out. They went in a door in the middle of the long bunk house, and found themselves in a sort of washroom. A stove made from a fifty-gallon oil drum stood in the middle, and on top of it was a wash boiler for heating water. Along the back wall was a trough running the length of the wall with eight or ten tin wash basins and pitchers in it, and at the end was a barrel of cold water. From the studding hung a couple of small, cracked mirrors and a razor strop. That was all.

From either side opened the long bunk rooms. Rows of cots were set side by side along the walls. Against the walls overhead were long shelves for personal plunder. At the farther end of either room was a heating stove set in a box of sand and cigarette butts, and a rough pine table with some Western Story magazines scattered on it.

31

Lumbercamp

Whistle Punk stood in the door a minute sniffing. The bunk-house smell was something new to him. It seemed to be made up of about equal parts of stale tobacco smoke, dust, the sour smell of sweat-soaked clothes and leather, and the smell of coal oil from the cans the legs of the cots stood in. Those cans puzzled him for a bit, till the bull cook, seeing him looking at them, spoke up.

"Them's t' keep varmints of one kind and another from clawin' their way into yore soogans," said he.

By that time Baldy had located a vacant cot for him, showed him where the mattresses were piled in a corner under a tarpaulin, and told him to "Grab a root an' growl!"

So Whistle Punk struggled manfully with mattress, blankets and a piece of old tarp', trying to put together something that would at least look like a bed. Meanwhile, Baldy made a few cautious passes at the litter on the floor with a mangy-looking broom, while explaining that he got kicked by a horse some time back, and that was why he was bull cooking. Mostly he was a skinner, he claimed.

"Bull cookin'?" said Whistle Punk, plumb goggle-eyed. "Are there special cooks for just cookin' bulls?"

"Naw," said Baldy, tickled green to find someone

that knew less than he did. "The bull cook carries wood and water for the cooks and looks after the bunk houses and stuff. Reckon yuh think a skinner skins horses; but he don't. A skinner is a teamster, usin' his team for haulin' or skiddin' logs."

"Gosh!" said Whistle Punk.

Seeing that the kid was impressed more than a little, Baldy went on. "Skinnin' don't amount t' shucks, hereabouts, son. Any greenhorn kin git him a job, almost. Now up in Orygon, things is different. Up there I'm knowed as Tree-Stretcher Burke. Reckon you might be interested in hearin' about that."

Without waiting to find out, he continued. "The way it come about is like this. The Bull o' the Woods comes round one day with an eeficiency feller. City geezer he was, out figgerin' ways t' save the company money. Fancy Pants we called him on account of the trick britches he wore with big, high ridin' boots. Little cooky-duster musstashe he had, too.

"Anyways, he looks at the little team I'm a-skiddin'

with, pony stock, they was, weighin' about eleven
hunderd each, an' right away allows as how they'd
have t' be got rid of. Reckoned as how they was too
light t' keep up with the bigger hosses on the job."

By this time Whistle Punk was sitting right on
the edge of his bunk, plumb pop-eyed with admira-
tion. Baldy hooked his thumbs in his galluses and
leaned back comfortably in a chair.

"I tell yuh, Bub," he went on, "thet gets my dander
up fer shore. Them ponies was like childern t' me,
an' I'd got 'em t' where they was so smart I didn't
need t' even use the ribbons with 'em. Jest talked t'
'em like I'm a-talkin' t' you this very minute, told
'em jest whut it was I wanted done, an' they'd do
'er. The only thing they couldn't do was hitch the
chain onto a log. But at any rate, as I was a-sayin',
my dander's up, so I offer t' bet a dollar an' a quarter
thet I kin skid more logs in an hour than any other
team in camp, regardless of size. Well, sir, they take
me up on that, an' pick a team t' work against me.
The teamsters, sawyers, swampers an' everybody in

sight gathers round t' see the fun. The Bull o' the Woods pulls out his big Waterbury watch thet ticks so loud thet it deefens three men permanent, an' we get busy. At the end of half an hour I'm only three logs ahead due to havin' bust a double-tree on the first haul, so I'm workin' mighty fast. We're skiddin' from right on the edge of the canyon rim, which drops straight down from the edge two hunderd an' four feet t' the bottom. I get my next log, which is layin' right on the edge of th' cliff, an' whilst lookin' t' see whut the other feller is a-doin', I slap a hitch onto the end of her with my chain an' holler giddap t' my hosses. They lean into the collars like good fellers, but although they strain fit t' bust a hamestrap, nothin' happens. That surprises them an' me too, so thinkin' that maybe they're soldierin' on me, I gives them a taste of the line. That hurts their feelin's more than a little, bein' as I never touch them, ordinarily, an' they flatten out till yuh can't throw yore hat under their bellies. Finally they get movin', but all th' way to the landin' they have t' scratch like sixty. I'd never seen 'em work so hard on any kind of pull. But bein' in a hurry I don't look back till I get clean up t'

the decks and hear the fellers begin t' holler. Then I look back t' see whut's a-causing all the fuss, an' whut I see durn near makes me swaller my chaw."

Lumbercamp

"What had happened, Mr. Baldy?" said Whistle Punk, who by this time was practically breathless from excitement.

"Well, Bub, dunno as you'll believe me, but by grab, in my hurry I'd made a little miscue, an' instead of hitchin' onto the log, durned if I didn't hitch onto the top of an old bull pine growin' in the bottom of the canyon with its top stickin' up over the canyon rim, right by the log I'm after. An' I'm a pie-eatin' doodlebug, son, if them ponies ain't gone an' jest stretched thet there tree the hull two hundred an' fifty yards to the landin' jest like it was taffy! Had 'er stretched out so she hummed like a fiddlestring. Well sir, thet there fancypants feller jest stood there with his jaw hangin' slack, while I took another chaw an' allowed as how that was a fair pull. There ain't nothin' more said about gettin' rid of that team, you can bet yore boots on that, an' the tree when it was cut up after bein' stretched made seven hundred an' fifty twelve-foot saw logs, I think it was, so I win the bet hands down. But I had t' rustle up a new log

Tin Pants

chain, bein' as that one is pulled out till it's nearly a solid bar!"

With that Baldy wandered off, still looking mournful about the days that were gone, leaving Whistle Punk to wash up and go over to the commissary. He still didn't have the least idea about what a whistle punk was, so he kept his mouth shut, taking whatever the store-keeper offered him. But when the store-keeper said, "Reckon you'll be wantin' some tin pants," he boggled a bit saying "yes." To his considerable relief, he found that they were just heavy canvas-like material that doesn't snag easy in the woods. Later he found out that after they've been worn a while and gotten well coated with pitch, the name isn't so far wrong, at that.

He finally got all his stuff: long underwear, heavy shirts, mittens and a pair of heavy-laced boots, and was just starting out when the store-keeper spoke up.

"Hey, Bub, yuh most forgot these," he said, and handed the kid a roll of wire, a couple of dry batteries, a pushbutton and some other gadgets.

40

"Yessir!"

Whistle Punk sort of gulped and said, "Yessir!", but couldn't for the life of him figure what the stuff was for. But he tried not to let on, and staggered off to the bunk house to try on his new finery and think things over.

THAT evening when the men started coming in from the woods and were washing up and changing their clothes, Whistle Punk lay on his bunk hoping he looked like an old timer. And when the big bell at the mess hall rang for supper, and someone hollered "Grub pile!" he tore out with the rest.

Although he got off to a good start, he was one of the last ones into the mess hall, being as how he fell over the long calks in his boots every five or six steps, which delayed him considerably. Those calks were one thing he'd argued with the store-keeper about. From his reading he'd got the idea that everyone in lumber camps wore them. Later he found out they were no good here, since most of the work was on rocky hillsides, and he had to change to hobnails.

When he finally made the trip, everyone else was up to the table. One of the flunkies showed him his place, and right away he found he had another problem on his hands. It was figuring out how to get his feet over the bench and sit down between the two men on either side of him without gigging one or the other of them with his spikes. He finally made it

44

all right, but it took him several weeks of practice to do it clean and fast.

When he got settled he picked his tin cup off the tin plate that was turned upside down over his knife, fork and spoon, and was ready to get down to business. Every little way along the table was a big coffee pot, plates of bread, pans of meat, potatoes, and cans of condensed milk. Everybody reached for what he wanted. As the pans emptied the flunkies refilled them. Nobody talked. The only sound was the scraping of eating tools on the tin plates and the blowing of coffee. When time came for dessert, Whistle Punk looked around to see what to do, and found that the proper way was to mop out your plate with a piece of bread, and then take your pick of the stewed fruit, pudding or pie, putting it in your now clean plate.

As soon as a man finished he got right up and went outside to pick his teeth. Whistle Punk failed to notice that the proper thing was to carry your plate and cup along with you and put them on the big table by the door as you went out. But he wasn't

Lumbercamp

Whiffler

long in finding out his mistake and correcting it.

After supper most of the crew went back to the bunkhouse. Some played cards, one worried a French harp, while back in the corner a big teamster got busy on the third easy lesson on banjo playing. The rest laid around on their bunks looking through the mail order catalogs or stood around the stove growling about the work and wages, or telling about how they were going to ship to Alaska or some such place.

Whistle Punk hung around the fringe of the crowd, keeping his mouth shut, which was a mighty fine idea in a strange place. But when he heard a screech owl holler outside, he couldn't keep still any longer. "Whut kind of a critter was it thet jest hollered, do you reckon?"

Right away a gangling swamper by the name of Shikepoke spoke up. "Reckon thet's a Sidehill Whiffler, Bub," he said. "They's quite a lot of 'em round right now. Yuh wanta be on the lookout for 'em."

"Yeah?" said Whistle Punk, his eyes bugging out. "Are they dangerous?"

47

Lumbercamp

"Right smart. Thet's what happened t' the last whistle punk we had. He got careless an' one et him. Didn't leave nuthin' but the rivets from his pants. Yuh see, the Sidehill Whiffler is about the size of a razorback hog, an' twic't as mean. But the funny thing about him is that the legs on the north side of him are three and a quarter inches shorter than the ones on the south side. Thet way he has t' live on the sidehills, and kin go only one way round them, at thet. If'n he gits on level ground he tips over. Naturally thet don't help his disposition none."

Whiffle Stick

"If they're thet bad, Mister Shikepoke, why aren't you all carryin' guns?"

"It ain't no use gunnin' fer 'em, son. A bullet, unless it hits 'em right exactly between the eyes, will bounce right back and get yuh. We lost a timber cruiser thet way last winter, we did. No sir, they's only one way to deal with 'em. If'n yuh sees one comin' towards yuh, jest go on, pertendin' thet yuh don't notice it till it's exactly ten feet away. . . ."

"But how will I know when it's exactly ten feet?" said Whistle Punk.

"I was jest a-comin' t' thet, son. I was jest a-comin' t' thet. We have been around so long that we kin measure it exact with our eyes, but you'd better go over t' the stable the first thing in the mornin' an' get Filthy Bill here to cut yuh a ten-foot whiffle stick from one of his whiffle trees. Then yuh will always be prepared.

"But as I was a-sayin', when he's jest ten feet off, yuh jump six feet up hill. The Whiffler will rush by before he can stop, then when he tries t' turn round and come back after yuh, he will have t' turn with his short legs down hill, and at the second step he'll fall on his side an' slide to the bottom of the canyon! But in yore spare time yuh better practice jumpin' sideways all yuh can. It's liable t' come in handy!"

Whistle Punk look around at the dark corner back of him and edged up a little closer to the stove. The conversation for a while was mainly a business of exchanging horrible stories of close shaves with Whifflers. Each experience was a little more bloodcurdling than the last, until Whistle Punk's hair was standing up like the war lock on a Sioux Indian.

But pretty soon everybody started going to bed, and it wasn't long before everyone in the room seemed to be snoring, except him. Somehow he didn't sleep so well, but spent most of the night wondering if maybe this wasn't the wrong job for him, anyway.

CHAPTER IV: *Whiffle Stick. The Kid works himself into a Lather. Struggles up the Tote Road with his Equipment. What a Bulldozer is. Rosinbelly tops the Spar Tree. Is put to swamping.*

THE NEXT morning after breakfast, as the men left the mess hall, they went through a small side room where there was a long table piled with bread, meat, pie and cake. They took their lunch pails from a shelf and made up whatever kind of lunches they wanted.

After Whistle Punk had packed his and got outside, the boss told him that they were going to top out a new spar tree, and for him to grab an axe and go help Shikepoke swamp out for Rosinbelly, the high climber who was going to do the topping.

As soon as the boss was out of hearing, Shikepoke spoke up. "Got yore whiffle stick, Bub?"

"Yessir!" said Whistle Punk. "Reckon this'll do?"

Lumbercamp

"Well, now, I dunno fer sure. Lemme see 'er." Then he called some more of the men over and asked them what they thought about it. Some thought it was a bit short and some others thought it should be a bit longer, so they finally decided to leave it just as it was. But to make absolutely sure that he knew how to use it, they had him practice. One of the crew would pretend he was the Whiffler and have the kid practise jumping sidewise as soon as he came in reach of the stick. They kept him jumping sidewise till he was most worn out, and the day not yet started.

By the time he was all in a lather of sweat, it was time to start for work, so away they went with Whistle Punk struggling along with his lunch bucket, a double-bitted axe and the whiffle stick. He figured that he was a full-fledged woods pussy for certain sure.

But there wasn't much time to admire himself, as they went up the canyon. The sun was just hitting the tops of the hills, but it was still fairly dark down where they were, and frostier than all get out.

54

Bulldozer

Up ahead the teamsters were already under way, each man riding one of his horses, with his canvas water bag, lunch bucket, grain sack and cant hook slung on the other.

At first they followed a well-used tote road, lined with decked-up logs waiting to be hauled down to the railroad. Whistle Punk had expected to see the cut-over hills looking plumb bare, but Shikepoke told him that this was Government reserve, and that the forest ranger went ahead and marked the trees to be cut, leaving the small stuff for reforestation.

After about a mile, they turned off up a side canyon along a new road being cut out with a bulldozer. He'd heard about this machine, and had supposed it was some kind of contraption for taming bulls. But it was nothing but a big blade fastened to the front end of a big caterpillar tractor, for plowing out roads. When they came up to it, the driver was down under it with a bunch of wrenches looking for trouble and muttering to himself, while the swampers cleared out the jackpines ahead.

Lumbercamp

Rosinbelly

From there on it wasn't far to the top of the ridge where the spar tree was. While Rosinbelly was getting his climbing irons on and his tools collected, Shikepoke and Whistle Punk started swamping out a space around the base of the tree where the donkey engine was to be. At least Shikepoke did considerable swamping. Whistle Punk spent most of his time trying to get his axe unwedged from a too-slanting cut or looking to see what kind of nick he had put in the blade when he hit the last rock. By the time he'd get a three-inch jackpine cut through it would look like it had been chewed off. "Gophering," Shikepoke called it.

It wasn't long before Rosinbelly was ready to go to work. He wore a pair of lineman's climbing irons and a wide leather safety belt into which he hooked his climbing rope. This rope had a wire cable in the center and was fastened to a ring on one side of the belt. The other end was passed round the tree and brought through a bulldog catch on the other side of the belt. This catch is a gadget that lets the rope

Lumbercamp

come through to take up slack, but prevents it from sliding back.

As soon as he got everything adjusted, Rosinbelly dug in his irons and started climbing, hitching the loop up a foot or two at a time as he climbed. His saw and axe hung on small ropes from his belt, swinging several feet below him, so as to be out of his way when he climbed. When he reached the first branch he readjusted his loop, set his spikes firmly and leaned back against his safety belt. That way his hands were free to use the axe chopping off the branches. He worked round and round the trunk as he went up, cutting off all the limbs until he got to where the top was to be cut out.

Whistle Punk and Shikepoke got back to watch.

"This here job is plenty dangerous," Shikepoke told the kid. "It takes a perfectly still day and lots of nerve. When he cuts thet top loose, yuh see, the kickback makes the top of the spar he's a-hangin' onto buck like a bay steer. It's no soft job hangin' onto it with nothing but a lot of vacant space below yuh.

59

Lumbercamp

Riggers Next

An' if'n a gust of wind should come along at just the wrong minute it's apt t' twist the top so the trunk splits an' squeezes the highclimber inside his safety belt till he's no good t' nobody."

Whistle Punk was so excited he almost forgot to keep in reach of his whiffle stick, and when the top finally gave way and came whistling down to land with a crash that could be heard half a mile, his face was white as a sheet. He had no ambition to be a highclimber at all.

While he and Shikepoke cleared out the wreckage of the top, Shikepoke told him that the riggers would come along next and haul up a big iron cap to be put on top of the spar, and run guy cables out in all directions to brace it. Then they would place the big blocks, run the high lead cables through them, and set up the donkey engine.

Meanwhile they had finished there and were put with a crew of swampers clearing landings, so Whistle Punk got to see considerable of the workings. The trees, he found out, are cut by a falling

crew. They work in pairs. When they pick their tree, one notches it deeply with an axe on the side towards which it is to fall, while the other gives the saw a few squirts of coal oil from a bottle he carries in his hip pocket. That takes off the coating of pitch so the saw won't bind. The sawing itself is hard work, as most

62

Slashings

of the time you either have your head almost down between your knees or else you are hunkered down like a dog licking a pot.

Whistle Punk expected to see the sawyers run like everything to get out of the way as soon as the tree started to fall, but all they did was pull the saw out as soon as the tree started to lean, and step back a step or two to watch it fall.

The tree would slowly lean a little farther and a little farther, then suddenly, seeming to have definitely made up its mind, it would really start falling with a swish that ended up almost a whistle, followed by a big crash and a cloud of dirt when it finally hit the ground. It would quiver all over and twitch a few times like a live thing, then lay still.

After that the branches have to be chopped off, the top cut out, the trunk bucked up into log lengths, and the tops and branches, or slashings, piled up.

Later the skidders come along, some using one horse and some two. They hitch onto the logs with a chain, and drag or skid them, one or two at a time, to

Lumbercamp

the nearest landing where they can be picked up and hauled to the railroad. These horses really know their business, climbing over stumps and rocks where a goat would have trouble, and a good teamster babies his team like they were part of his family.

Nevertheless, he takes no back talk from them, for a smart horse, if he finds it's possible to run a whizzer on you, will get so that on any pull he doesn't like the looks of he will seem to strain fit to bust something, while really not pulling enough to haul the hat off your head—just waiting for you to get someone else to hook on and help. But if he finds you stand for no foolishness, he'll lay out and pull like a whitehead, and look proud as a speckled pup about it all.

After spending a few days doing this, Whistle Punk was all blistered and stove up from swinging an axe and was plenty anxious to start doing something else.

WHISTLE Punk had been in

camp a week or so, when the boss stopped him as he came from the mess hall after breakfast.

"Grab yore wires an' the rest of yore dyflinkuses," he said, "an' go up t' the high lead. We're a-goin' t' start 'er up t'day."

So Whistle Punk tore over to the bunk house where he had cached his stuff, then hightailed it for the timber. Finally he was going to start being a whistle punk!

When he got to where they had topped the spar tree, he found the rigging all in place and the donkey engine set up. The donkey man, a lantern-jawed individual called Step-and-a-Half because of his jerky walk, was already getting up steam.

Lumbercamp

He showed the kid how to hook up his gadgets to the whistle and fasten the wires to them so that when he pushed the little button it blew the whistle.

"All right, Bub, now you climb up there on the ridge with yore wire, to a place where yuh kin see the whole length of the cable, an' fix you a place t' set."

So Whistle Punk rolled out his wire till he came to a good place, and set down his board with the push button fastened to it.

Soon the donkey man came up to explain things to him. "We use a high lead or else a dragline, which is about the same except thet the cable runs along the ground instead of overhead like this, fer gettin' logs outta pockets where there ain't no tote road," he said. "Yuh see the cable runs out from this spar t' thet one acrost the way, an' back agin through them blocks and down t' the winch on the donkey. It's the same idee as the clothes lines yuh see outta windows in the city."

He stopped to squirt a stream of tobacco juice at

a tumble bug that was rolling a ball of something or other along a path about six or eight feet away. He frowned at missing the first time, being vain of his marksmanship, but scoring a bull's eye the second time cheered him up, although the tumble bug didn't seem so enthusiastic.

That taken care of, he went on. "I run the cable out, an' the fellers hook on a log or two, an' I hauls 'er back. But from down there I can't see the cable, so when the log is snared on, the straw boss will wave t' yuh an' yuh quick push this button twic't. Then I know that she's ready t' go. But in case a log gets snagged on the way over, 'er anything else happens thet looks like it hadn't orter, yuh right away gimme three whistles so I kin stop 'er!"

After a few more warnings about not messing up equipment by giving wrong signals, he went back to the donkey, leaving Whistle Punk to soak up the early sun while he waited to go to work.

Way off below him he could see the camp buildings, looking like matchboxes. The sun was just hit-

Lumbercamp

ting the bunk houses, while the mess hall and the cook shack with its feather of pale smoke was still in shadow. The air was so clear he imagined he could hear the bull cook muttering to himself as he crossed the road to the bunk house.

There wasn't time for much woolgathering, however. The crew soon showed up, ready for work. As soon as the first log was hooked on, the straw boss waved his arms over his head, and Whistle Punk punched the button twice, and watched the two little puffs of steam shoot up a few seconds before he could hear the whistle. Then a bigger plume shot straight up in the air from the exhaust as the donkey went into action, drawing in the cable and the logs.

That was all he had to do—just sit up there and relay signals. He was kind of nervous about it at first for fear he would give the wrong signal, but that soon wore off and he settled down to being a whistle punk.

They were hauling about a quarter of a mile here, and he thought it was pretty wonderful, until he happened to speak of it as they ate lunch that noon. At that, Step-and-a-Half looked up from his dinner bucket.

"So you think this is something, do you, Bub?" said he, and turned to Shikepoke. "Tell him about the real outfit we rigged up for Paul Bunyan that time."

"Well, sir," said Shikepoke, "one winter we're workin' for Ol' Paul, when he discovers that one cuttin' crew thet he's forgotten about has gone an' cut logs clear down t' Kansas. Now that's too far t' build a tote road, an' Paul has just about decided t' mark that timber and time off his books, when John-nie Inkslinger, his bookkeeper, suggests buildin' a dragline t' haul them up. At first Paul don't think much of the idea, but a couple days later he comes round and tells the Bull o' the Woods to pick him a crew and go t' work.

"There ain't no need of goin' into all the details of the buildin' of that outfit, an' the trouble we had rig-gin' it an' all, but the spar trees was shipped in special from the northeast corner of Sweden. Two mile an' a quarter high they was. Took three four-masted ships an' a rowboat t' git 'em across the ocean. Bein' as how there was no cable big enough or long enough, Paul and his riggers spun their own from barb wire. It kept five hundred and nine flunkies busy their spare time just cuttin' the barbs off. When it was all rigged up an' done that crew of riggers went East and used the trick Paul showed them, making cables for suspension bridges. In the meantime, Ole, the blacksmith, had built a special high-geared donkey engine that could haul a log clean up from Kansas in two minutes an' a quarter. Bein' such a long ways, one whistle punk couldn't see the signals, so it took seven lookin' together to make it. After the logs was hauled out, Paul fastened a stage coach body t' the cable and did a thrivin' business haulin' freight and passengers from Kansas to Chicago till the railroad come along and took the business away from him."

"Gosh!" said Whistle Punk, and then the whistle blew and everyone went back to work.

73

CHAPTER VI: *Forest Fire! Whistle Punk is rarin' to go. Call comes for more Men. Digs Fire Guards in Heat and Smoke. Almost trapped. Decides there's no Fun in Fire Fighting.*

ONE DAY late in the fall, just before the first snow-fall, Whistle Punk noticed a big cloud of black smoke rising to the northwest. The first chance he got he went down and asked Step-and-a-Half about it.

"Yeah, I seen it, Bub," said he. "Reckon from the looks it must be a little forest fire over t'ords the Limestone."

"D'yuh suppose we'll hafta go fight it?" Whistle Punk asked hopefully.

"Not unless she gits a heap of a sight worse, I reckon," the donkey man answered. "She's a purty fur piece off."

There wasn't time for more powwow, as Whistle Punk had to hump himself to get back up on the hill before he was missed. But all day he hopefully watched the cloud of smoke grow larger and blacker. At times big clouds of yellowish brown smoke would roll up to mix with the black.

That night after supper most of the men climbed to the ridge back of camp for a look. The glow from the flames was plainly reflected on the clouds of smoke, although the fire was fully fifteen miles off. At times, when the fire came up over a ridge, the flames themselves were in plain sight.

Whistle Punk was about to have a conniption fit, he was that excited. Then, to top it all off, the mess hall bell started ringing fit to wake the dead. There was plenty of excitement then, for that meant that the boss was calling all the men in.

By the time they got back to the bunk house all the trucks in camp had been brought and were being loaded with axes, picks, shovels and even garden rakes. Word had finally come in that more men were needed to handle the fire, so the whole crew was being sent.

Smoke

Whistle Punk made sure to get in the same truck with Shikepoke, and they tore out. He found out then the reason for all the fire trails he'd seen. These are narrow roads cut through all possible parts of the timber, so that in case of a fire, men and equipment can be hauled in close to the trouble with the least possible loss of time.

As they got closer to the fire the smoke grew thicker and thicker until at times the head-lights of the trucks didn't penetrate more than a few feet, and the smoke swirled in the beams like fog. The men began to cough and choke.

Shikepoke hollered to the kid over the roar of the motor and rattle of tools. "If'n yuh think this is bad, wait till we really git t' work. Meanwhile soak yore handkerchief an' tie it over yore face!"

Whistle Punk got out his handkerchief, and Shikepoke soaked it with water from one of the canvas water bags. With it over his nose it was easier to breathe, but there was no way to stop his eyes from smarting and streaming tears.

Lumbercamp

It wasn't long after that until they came upon a ridge from which they could see the fire. It seemed to be several miles long. Silhouetted against the flames they could see men feverishly at work.

"Looks like a mighty bad one!" Shikepoke hollered to the kid. "Yuh better keep clost t' me when we git there. Thet ain't no place t' be millin' round alone!"

Fire Guards

"Yessir!" said Whistle Punk, not half as enthusiastic about fighting fire as he had been.

A little farther along they came to the forest ranger in charge of the business. Everyone unloaded and waited to be told what to do. This was Government land, and in case of fire everyone, farmers, miners, road crews as well as lumberjacks were supposed to turn out and help if necessary, under the direction of the forest rangers.

The men from Fifteen were finally told to grab axes and shovels and were put to work making a fire break along a little meadow that ran parallel to the fire. It was hot, backbreaking work. While part of the crew with axes swamped out the brush, Whistle Punk and the rest dug a wide trench down through the leaf mould to solid dirt. Fire will run along the ground through the pine needles and leaves. By ditching that way, then stationing men all along to beat out any fire that jumps the ditch, it can be stopped—sometimes.

It was hot work. The wind brought the heat of the

fire to them so that as it got closer the sweat poured off them in streams and every breath seemed to scorch all the way down. Soon live embers began falling about them and on their clothes, which didn't make them any more comfortable. Besides, there was the business of having to watch any little fires that started from the blowing brands, and beating them out before they got big enough to be dangerous.

They worked till it seemed they were ready to drop, then other men took their places while they straggled back to the truck for a drink and a few minutes rest. After a little they were back in their places.

After the short rest Whistle Punk thought he was worse off than before. His muscles all seemed cramped, and his hands so sore he could hardly hold his shovel. But he kept on the best he could, until, when they had their ditch about done, a ranger came by and took half the crew away to another part of the fire.

Whistle Punk and Shikepoke were among the

ones moved. They were taken to the far side of a canyon and put to swamping and dragging out slashings along the rim. The wind showed signs of dying down, and if it did there was a chance of keeping the fire from jumping across when it got to the other rim. If they could do that and the other fire guard they had been working on held, they would have the main part of the fire stopped. But there was no time to lose, and they slipped and slid, and scrambled over the rocky ground till they were so tired they didn't know whether they were afoot or on horseback.

After what seemed hours, they saw the fire coming over the ridge across from them. As it hit the hogback the wind suddenly freshened and the fire swooped up and into the tops of a heavy stand of big pines. That was what is called a crown fire, Shikepoke told Whistle Punk.

"Watch 'er sail through those tops. She's travellin' faster'n a horse kin run!" Shikepoke had to holler over the roar of the fire. "If'n something don't

81

Lumbercamp

happen quick she'll jump clear over the canyon an' ketch back of us!"

The heat by that time had become unbearable and the men were all sent back out of the way, there being nothing they could do in the face of it. It looked as if they had all their work to do over again, but just as they scrambled up onto the fire trail, a few drops of rain spattered down. In a few minutes a pretty heavy downpour was on them, and none too soon, either. Another quarter of an hour and the fire would have jumped the canyon. As it was, it sputtered and sizzled as it worked into the wet branches. Before long there was nothing to be seen but an occasional big tree or stump that burned, although big clouds of steam and smoke rose up from the ground where the thick mat of pine needles still smouldered.

The big danger was past, but the work was not over by a long shot. Crews would have to work all night ditching around fires that were too deep in the litter to be put out by the rain. Otherwise they might smoulder for days, and then break out again.

Lumbercamp

The crew from Fifteen, having come the farth-
est, were sent back first. Whistle Punk was plenty
glad to climb up into the truck, and before they had
it turned around he was sound asleep on a pile of
gunnysacks on the bottom. They got into camp just
at daylight.

They climbed out as best they could with their

stiffened muscles and went to the mess hall for coffee before going to wash up. A strange looking crew they were. Their faces were blackened till no one was recognizable, eyebrows were singed off, and their clothes were all burned full of little holes.

"Wanta go out an' fight fire today, Bub?" Shikepoke asked him.

"Nossir!" said Whistle Punk, grinning with the side of his face that felt the least burned. "Reckon I've had plenty." And he stumbled off to the bunk house to go to bed, only about ten steps ahead of the rest of the crew, at that.

DURING the fall Whistle Punk

had enjoyed his job. It was nice sitting up there where he could see out over the canyons, and the leaves turning all colors. Once or twice he even saw deer on the hillsides.

But after snow came it was a horse of a different color. The biggest job was keeping his feet warm, sitting still the way he had to. But he got him a pair of big felt boots with four-buckle overshoes, and things didn't seem so bad. And he was getting a pretty good idea of the way the logging business worked.

From where he was he could see the logs being loaded for the trip down to the railroad landing above camp. During the fall most of the hauling was done with trucks, but after snow came they used bob-sleds or one of the big cats.

The tote roads being mostly downhill, a single team was able to haul an enormous big load of logs. After a few trips the snow was packed as hard as ice, and there being no brakes on a bobsled, the trips were pretty exciting.

One noon when Whistle Punk happened to speak of this, Pete Prestjohn was reminded of a time he was hauling for an outfit up in Oregon.

"We was haulin' five mile," said he, "all of it down-hill. Well, sir, we usta sprinkle water on that tote road every night so she'd be iced up proper, come mornin'. After we got loaded an' chained, we skin-ners allus tied our ear flappers down tight, because the wind going down was somethin' fierce. Yuh see, after the load was once started she kept gatherin' speed constant, with no more pullin' from the hosses till we musta been doin' all of sixty, seventy miles an hour. Well naturally it's purty hard fer the hosses to keep out ahead of a rig travellin' like that, so we

was all the time losin' teams. But after a while we get the idea of buildin' platforms of planks on the tongues of the sleds, so the hosses, as soon as they'd got the load well started, could jump up an' ride the rest of the way.

"It was really a sight to see those big bobs, with forty or fifty logs on, come tearin' into the valley in a cloud of snow, the skinner bracin' himself fer all he's worth up on the top, an' steerin' with a big sweep, an' the hosses rared back on their platforms with their manes an' tails a-flyin' in the wind! They really

89

enjoyed it. Got so's they wouldn't work fer any skinner thet wouldn't let 'em ride, they did!"

"Gosh!" said Whistle Punk, and for several days he seriously considered going off to one of those camps where they did things in such an exciting way. But then payday came along, and he had other things to worry about.

Word had spread that the eagle was going to scream and Whistle Punk was in line with the rest of the men, waiting his turn at the paymaster's window, when the boss came by.

"Whatter you doin' here?" he wanted to know.

"It's payday, ain't it?" the kid asked.

"Yeah, but not fer you."

"How come?" the kid wondered, getting kind of worried.

"Thet new outfit of yores ain't paid fer yet," the boss told him. "But if'n you don't buy nothin' else next month you should have about a dollar and a dime comin' next payday."

"Oh gosh!" said Whistle Punk, and he went over

to the bunk house to think that one over. Most of the men were going to town to spend their pay, and they offered to take him along, but he figured he'd just as soon stay around camp.

The next day there weren't enough men in camp to work in the woods, so at breakfast the boss told Whistle Punk to go out with the jammer crew loading log cars.

He grabbed himself a cant hook and his lunch, and followed the crew up the track to the big landing. The log train wasn't there yet, so Jaybird Smith, the straw boss, put him to work rolling logs up to where

91

the loading crew would be able to hook onto them. That was easy and before long he figured he was plenty far ahead, and being as how the little loco-motive was just coming in sight with the log train he thought he might as well sit down and rest a bit. So he sat himself comfortably on one of the timbers the logs were decked up on, and leaned back against the pile to look things over.

He'd been wondering about the jammer for some time. From the sound of the name he figured it must be quite an exciting contraption, but when it got there he found that it was just another donkey en-gine with a boom for loading logs, mounted on a sled arrangement. The whole kit and kaboodle was set on the first car with the boom hanging out over the boiler of the locomotive.

While he watched, the train was spotted, and a cable was taken back from the jammer and hooked to a car a couple of lengths back. The other end was hitched to the winch on the donkey, and then, by winding in the cable, the whole shooting match slid

Growed Fast!

from the first car to the second, and they were ready to start loading.

Jaybird looked over to where Whistle Punk was resting, and hollered, "Haul out of it! This ain't no rest cure you're takin'!"

Whistle Punk started to jump up, but nothing happened. It seemed like he couldn't haul the seat of his pants loose from the timber he was sitting on. The more he tried the less luck he had. His collar seemed to be getting tighter and tighter, till finally he was sitting so far down on the middle of his back that he couldn't get his feet under him to do any good. About that time he commenced to get scared, and much as he hated to do it, hollered for help.

The crew took a look at him all sprawled out with his feet and arms waving in the air, and gathered round to offer suggestions. Some suggested that he try pulling himself loose by his boot straps. Others figured that he'd grown to the log and that there was no hope of saving him.

Squeaky spoke up. "Remember this happenin'

Lumbercamp

Scared Spitless

onc't before, I do. Up in Maine where I was a-workin' one time. Feller got in the same perdikiment yo're in now. We couldn't get him loose, an' fed him with a spoon for a while, but he finally froze to death, he did. Growed plumb tight t' the log, he did. Nobody ever did know whut caused it, but there ain't no cure that I knows of."

By this time Whistle Punk was scared plumb spitless. The more he struggled the tighter he seemed to be fastened to the log. And the crew were having themselves a mighty fine time, till Jaybird came along. Seeing what was going on, he was plenty sore. He was very conscientious, like most straw bosses, and hated to see the company's time wasted.

He let out considerable of a holler. "All right, you geezers! Roll thet log off'n the kid's coat-tail, and let's get some logs loaded!"

There was considerable activity around there then. The engineer tore out and climbed up into the cab where he muttered among his gadgets, the donkey man climbed the jammer like a squirrel climbing

95

Lumbercamp

a tree, and Squeaky rolled the log back, letting the kid up. Whistle Punk was plenty relieved to find that he hadn't grown fast to anything, but that the log back of him had simply rolled over on his coat-tail while he was sitting there, so he couldn't get up. He was some time living that down, and after that wore his coat inside his overalls so it wouldn't happen again. Naturally he felt kind of silly about the whole business.

Jammer

As he went back to rolling logs, the donkey started chattering, letting the cable out. It had a sort of bridle on the end, with two hooks that hooked into each end of the log, like ice tongs into a cake of ice, and the log was hauled up over the car. The top loader grabbed it with his cant hook and eased it down to where he wanted it on the load. Two men with lead lines on each of the hooks held the log back so it wouldn't swing too far and knock the top loader galley west.

As soon as each car was loaded, it was chained tight, and the jammer pulled back to another car, until it sat on the last one, where it was left until next day. Then it would be hooked to the front end of the next empty string, to load it.

At first Whistle Punk thought he would like to be a top loader, but after a while he found that the job was no cinch after all. Loading those cars was a delicate business. If the weight wasn't distributed just right, the whole car might turn turtle on a rough curve, and that is a thing that brings complaints

Lumbercamp

from the train crews. So he decided maybe his job
was all right, as long as he could keep his tail-feathers
out from under the logs.

CHAPTER VIII: *Whistle Punk finally gets his Pay and goes to Town. Takes a Bellyflop into the Mill Pond. Goes through the Big Sawmill with Shikepoke. Sees the Logs sawed into Lumber. Haircut, city Style.*

ONE PAY day after Whistle Punk had been around camp three or four months, he decided to ride the log train to town with the rest of the men and see what became of the logs after they got to the big mill.

So, with their pay in their pockets, they swarmed over the little locomotive for the ride down the canyon to town. There were so many of them going that only a few could get places in the cab, the rest having to climb on wherever there was space. Some sat up on top of the tender, some on the front step, and the rest had to hang on as best they could on the cat walk running on either side of the boiler. That was a nice warm place. Hot enough to singe the hair off a solid brass dog, Whistle Punk decided after they'd gone a few miles. He was sitting about halfway between the cab and the smokestack. Every time the engineer whistled for a curve or crossing the scalding water from the whistle spattered down his neck, and in narrow places in the canyon the bushes scraped so close that he was sure they'd scrape him off. Then, to make things worse, every time the fireman put a couple of scoops of sand through the flues to clean out the soot, the force of the exhaust carried it up through the stack and sprinkled it all over the men on the outside. Being as it was all covered with gummy tar by the time it got outside, it was not any too pleasant to have around.

But the men in the cab were not much better off, he saw. Those hobnails they were wearing didn't help their footing on the greasy steel of the gangway. And the engineer didn't help them, either. He would mosey along till he got right to a curve, then open the throttle a bit. The little extra speed was usually enough to cause the whole crowd to slide into a corner and fall all over themselves.

102

Big as Life

Early in the afternoon they pulled into the mill yard, with Whistle Punk sitting up by the boiler looking big as life and twice as natural. He cocked his cap back over one ear as they passed the office windows to look like the rest of the men.

They spotted the train on the track beside the mill pond, and the locomotive was taken away. The kid climbed down and looked himself over to see if he was still all there, and was somewhat surprised to find that he had no holes burned in him. Then he looked the place over, finding it somewhat different from the first time he had seen it.

Big clouds of steam were swirling up where the exhaust from the engines in the big mill bubbled into the pond. Trucks wound in and out of the place, and big straddlers carrying piles of lumber hugged up against their bellies bumbled here and there. Out on the high tramways little white mules and stubby little trucks pushed or hauled buggies of lumber about. Over all was the thin whine of the bandsaws from the big mill and the scream of the planers and

103

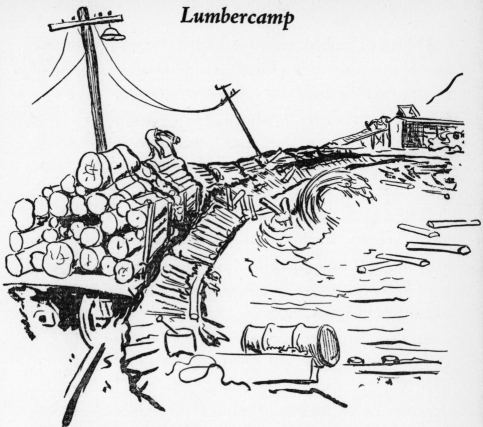

the moulding mill. The cyclones drawing ground-up waste to the fuel house added their heavy hum. And a fine mist of white sawdust, flour-fine, settled on everything. The air seemed thick with the hot, sour smell of the mill pond.

104

Bronc' Log

Whistle Punk stood around a while watching the cars being unloaded. A man at each end of the train unchained the load, then loosened the stakes on the side next the water, letting the top logs roll into the pond. The splash they made entertained Whistle Punk more than a little. Then the bottom ones were rolled off with a cant hook.

After that was done and the men gone away, Whistle Punk figured that no one was watching him, and it might be a good time to try riding some of the logs floating out in the pond, like he'd seen pictures of lumberjacks doing.

So he jumped out onto one that looked big enough to hold him, and right away got the surprise of his life. Not knowing how to bring his weight straight down as he lit, he found himself off balance on a log that was rolling and bucking like a bay steer. The faster he scrambled to get his feet on top the faster the log rolled. He hadn't realized that a log could be so lively or so slippery. One minute his feet would be almost slipping off on one side, then he'd scramble

Lumbercamp

back and find himself down on the other side. The blamed log simply wouldn't stay still, and he was getting pretty much fed up with the whole business, but didn't just see what he was going to do about it. Finally he lost his balance entirely, and did a good old-fashioned bellyflop into the water, boots and all. He thought he was gone gosling for sure by that time, but when he came up, somebody hollered, "Ride 'em, cowboy!" and he felt himself hauled out by the slack of his britches.

As soon as he finished spitting out the mouthful of bark and stuff he'd picked up when he fell, he looked up to discover it was Shikepoke that had gotten him out of trouble.

"Yo're a purty-lookin' sight, now, ain't yuh?" said Shikepoke, grinning from ear to ear. "Better wear yore spurs next time." Then after showing the kid how it should be done, he went on, "If'n you've had enough swimmin', how about goin' over t' see the big mill work?"

"Sure thing! Yessir! Reckon it's all right?" said

Lumbercamp

Bull Chain

Whistle Punk, tickled pink but not wanting to seem too enthusiastic. They headed off around the pond.

"Yuh see," said Shikepoke, "they run thet there boom made of eight by eight timbers fastened to a chain, round a bunch of logs and draw them down t' this end of the pond where the pikeman on thet platform can reach them an' haul 'em in reach of the bull chain."

"Why is it called a bull chain?" Whistle Punk asked. "I'm all the time hearin' about bull gangs, bulldozers, bull wheels an' such like. How come?"

"Dunno fer sure why it is, Bub," said Shikepoke, kind of stumped by that one. "Prob'ly it's because of their size. A bull gang goes round doin' odd jobs of heavy work. Most likely it's the same with the rest of the stuff. Anyways, the bull chain is thet big endless chain yuh see runnin' up the trough from the water at the pikeman's feet, up to the top floor of the big mill. It has hooks every few feet, an' the pikeman pulls a floatin' log up till the hooks ketch one end of it an' pull it into the lower end of the trough. Once

there it rides clean up into the mill."

By that time they had gotten almost to the mill itself. They went around the big sawdust pile, and after narrowly escaping getting squashed by a little caterpillar tractor pulling a box car, they went up the

110

cat walk beside the bull chain and into the big mill.

Here they found plenty of noise and excitement. As the logs came up, all dripping wet, they were checked for the approximate number of board feet in them, and rolled off onto another set of chains that would take them to the saw carriage.

The saw carriage took Whistle Punk's eye in no uncertain way. It was probably twenty feet long, running on rails. Three men rode it as it travelled back and forth past the saw. As he watched, a log was rolled down the chains, onto the carriage, and the gripman set hooks that held the log solid, while the man in the middle threw a lever setting the thickness of the cut to be made. Then they all braced themselves for the ride. The outfit looked to be going about thirty miles an hour when it hit the saw. They tore right on by without slowing up and the saw screamed like a panther as it ripped a slab off the side of the log. The man tailing the saw grabbed the slab and sent it on its way down the conveyors to the sorters and resaws, while the carriage brought up

111

Lumbercamp

against a buffer, stopped, and returned to its starting point. Then the grips were loosened, and a big beam with blunt teeth, called the 'nigger,' came up beside the carriage to turn the log over so a slab could be cut from the other side. As soon as the log was squared it was sliced into planks, and another dripping log took its place.

Whistle Punk looked around trying to find where the rest of the saw was. All he could see was a ribbon of steel about eight inches wide and about four feet long coming up out of the floor and disappearing inside a housing overhead.

Shikepoke saw his look and hollered over the racket. "Thet's a bandsaw, Bub. An endless ribbon like, thet runs up over a bull wheel in thet housing overhead, then down round another one downstairs an' back up."

"Whut's thet feller doin' back there? Th' one thet's all the time wavin' his fingers round?" Whistle Punk pointed to a sadfaced individual sitting in a little cubby back by the bandsaw.

"He starts and stops the carriage, and handles the nigger an' the saw from there," said Shikepoke. "When he waves his fingers he's signalin' the man

113

Lumbercamp

on the carriage the thickness of the next cut. One finger means a one-inch board, two, a two-inch, an' so on."

A seemingly endless stream of logs came up the chain, were rolled onto the carriage, and sawed up. From there the lumber went over conveyors past sorters and graders. Different kinds were sent different ways. After it was graded it was hauled out into the yards to be piled up with thin strips separating each layer so air could circulate through the piles while it seasoned. Later, when it was thoroughly dried, it would be hauled back, some to be sold as rough lumber, and the rest to go through the planers for finished lumber, mouldings, boxes, and what not.

They stood and watched the work a while, then moseyed out into the yard, across the bridge and on up town, past the depot. Shikepoke stopped off at the Chink's eating house, and Whistle Punk went on to the barber shop, more than a little impressed by the whole business of lumbering.

As he climbed into the barber's chair, the barber looked him over.   **115**

"Howdy!" he said. "You're one of the jacks from Fifteen, ain't yuh?"

"Yep!" said Whistle Punk, expanding his chest

somewhat. "It's payday. Reckon yuh kin give me a hair cut, an' leave the sides purty heavy, city style. I might take a shave, too, whilst you're about it!"

"Yes, SIR!" said the barber, waving his neckcloth.